101 BRAINBENDER Puzzles

Illustrated by Andrew Geeson

Written by Natasha Cobbold

TOP THAT! Kids™

Copyright © 2004 Top That! Publishing plc,
Tide Mill Way, Woodbridge, Suffolk, IP12 1AP, UK
Top That! is a Registered Trademark of Top That! Publishing plc.
All rights reserved.
www.topthatpublishing.com

1. Paintbrush Puzzle

There are eight triangles in this six-pointed star. Move two brushes to make another six-pointed star, but with only six visible triangles.

2. Logic Puzzler

What is it about you that changes every year, always going up and never coming down?

3. Anagram Antics

Unscramble each of these words to find something in the picture.

CORS SISS scissors
HARM ME hammer
ROT RAP parrot
TO CORD

4. Number Search

Two numbers between one and twenty are missing from the box. Can you find them?

13 19

5. Baffling Bet

A man was sitting in a café enjoying a drink when the waiter came over to him and said "I'll bet you £1 that if you give me £2, I will give you £3 in return." The man was puzzled as he thought about it. Should he accept the bet or not?

6. Word Play

Look at the clues and see if you can make new words by changing just one letter in each of these words.

Change FORK to a kind of meat.
Change SHOW to the opposite of fast.
Change HARD to a thick type of paper.

7. Age Question

When asked how old she was, Rosie replied "In two years I will be twice as old as I was five years ago." How old is she?

8. Number Cross

Fill in the numbers in the number grid by solving the clues.

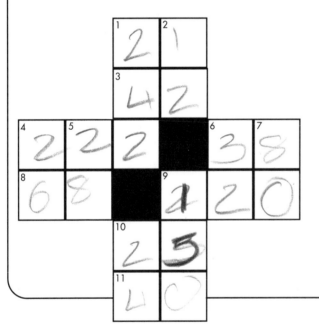

Across

1. Number of days in three weeks.
3. Six times seven.
4. 888 divided by four.
6. Half of seventy-six.
8. Four times seventeen.
9. Seven down plus eleven across.
10. 125 divided by five.
11. Eight + fourteen + eighteen.

Down

1. 121 doubled.
2. Thirty-six divided by three.
4. Half of fifty-two.
5. Eight across minus eleven across.
6. Four times eight.
7. Three across plus six across.
9. Half of 300.
10. Number of hours in a day.

9. Driving Dilemma

Bill was sitting in his car on an ordinary road pointing north. He turns to his friend and says "Even though we are pointing north, I can drive this car for one mile and end up one mile south of where we started from." How?

M	D	Y	T	A	F	W	U	Q	D	J	P
K	O	I	R	C	E	S	H	O	Z	K	S
T	B	U	J	O	C	I	G	L	B	D	Y
A	Z	Y	S	K	V	S	O	B	C	W	E
O	A	C	N	E	C	E	X	Y	I	N	K
G	I	P	L	K	F	S	N	A	C	R	N
F	O	S	J	F	T	D	D	O	F	L	O
H	R	C	A	W	I	B	K	S	I	Q	M
I	P	R	Q	U	X	N	T	H	P	L	X
K	I	Y	T	E	R	E	S	R	O	H	A
G	T	D	A	Z	C	I	O	J	U	C	B
R	W	A	O	F	L	X	B	D	R	I	B

10. Wild Wordsearch

Find these ten animals in the wordsearch.

GIRAFFE	HORSE
CAT	PIG
DOG	MONKEY
MOUSE	BIRD
LION	GOAT

11. Letter Change

Turn REAL into BELT by changing one letter at a time by following the clues.

1. Cotton and films come on this.
2. Sense of touch.
3. You walk on these.
4. A sort of pen tip.

REAL

_ _ _ _

_ _ _ _

_ _ _ _

_ _ _ _

BELT

12. Number Sequence

What's the next number in the sequence?

13. Ridiculous Riddle

Which source of heat is black when you buy it, red when you use it and grey when you throw it away? *coal*

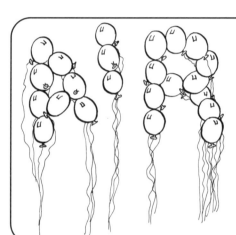

14. Alphabet Puzzle

Put a different letter or letters in front of the word AIR each time to solve the clues.

1. Strands of this are on your head.   H_AIR
2. At this you can go on different rides.   _AIR
3. You sit on this.   CH_AIR

15. Letter Assembler

Rearrange these letters to make a ten-letter word meaning 'all'.

THIEVE GRYN

16. What am I?

I am a word of five letters.
If you take away the first and last letters,
I will still sound the same.
Even if you take away the middle letter,
I will be the same as before.
What am I?

17. Mix and Match

Put the words below into their correct pairs.

Swan
Bear
Cow
Kangaroo
Rooster
Horse

Foal
Chick
Cygnet
Cub
Joey
Calf

18. Spot the Difference

Study the picture carefully for one minute. Then turn over the page and look at the same picture. Spot five things which have changed in the picture.

1. balloon
2. glasses
3. birds
4. bottle
5. Extra person in line

19. Solve the Mystery

It's the middle of winter and five pieces of coal, a carrot and a scarf are lying on the lawn. Nobody put them there but there is a perfectly good explanation why they are there. What is it?

20. Word Change

Look at the clues and make new words by changing just one letter in each of these words:

1. Change TALK into a story.
2. Change GATE into something found on a calendar.
3. Change FINE into a number.

21. Proverb Puzzler

Rearrange the letters to form a well-known six-word saying. As in the question, there are six letters in the first word of the answer, five letters in the second, three letters in the third, four letters in the fourth, two letters in the fifth and three letters in the sixth.

TRIKES HILWE ETH RONI SI THO

22. Number Cruncher

The number FIVE as written using block capitals contains exactly ten strokes or segments of a straight line. Can you find a number which, when written out as words, contains as many strokes as the number says. (Clue: it's between twenty and thirty.)

23. Word Wizz

Name the flowers that can be found by removing one letter from each word.

1. IRISH **2.** ROUSE

3. MASTER **4.** VIOLENT

24. Pencil Trick

Remove three pencils to leave three equal touching squares.

25. Letter Logic

What are the next four letters in the series? (Clue: there are twelve every year.)

J F M A M J J A

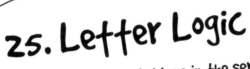

26. Countdown Conundrum

Seven men arrive at a meeting and each one shakes hands with all of the others. How many handshakes does that make?

27. Hidden Countries

In each of the sentences below, the name of a country is hidden. For example, the sentence: 'Interpol and the FBI catch criminals' contains the word Poland. Can you find them?

1. Our dog likes his food so much he eats a can a day.
2. Always use a pencil when drawing lines in diagrams.
3. The king was angry when a thief stole his painting.
4. Does the teacher teach in a classroom?
5. In anger, many people say things they don't mean.

28. Adder

Answer the clues, then create a new word by joining the two answers together. Can you think of any other words that are made up in this way?

NOISE OF A COW

\+   DANGER COLOUR

\=   SECURED LIKE A BOAT

29. Tricky Words

Which word can be put before all the words below to make four new words?

FAST THROUGH DOWN AWAY

30. How Did She Do That?

A woman went outside without an umbrella or a raincoat, yet did not get wet. How's that?

31. Upside Down

Which number, written in figures, increases in value by 21 when turned upside down it? (Clue: it's between 60 and 70)

32. Learn the Language

Think of words ending in –GRY. Angry and hungry are two of them. There are only three words in the English language. What is the third word? The word is something that everyone uses every day. If you have read carefully what is written, it already says what it is.

33. Match Them Up

Match up the pairs with their rightful owners.

34. Mind the Gap

Which single three-letter word completes all of the following words?

_for_WARD

BE _for_ E

_for_GED

IN_for_MATION

35. Oddly Enough

What is the opposite of NOT OUT?

OUT

36. Figure it out

Andy bought a bag of apples on Monday and ate a third of them. On Tuesday he ate half of the remaining apples. On Wednesday he looked in the bag to find he only had two apples left. How many apples were originally in the bag?

37. Date Dilemma

How many days is it from Wednesday 1st August to the first Saturday in September?

38. Missing Alphabet

Find the two letters missing from the ball.

39. Catch a Cat

If six cats can catch six rats in six minutes, how many cats are needed to catch ten rats in ten minutes?

40. Deadly Decision

An explorer is caught stealing food by a tribe who order that he must die. But the tribe chief is a reasonable man and allows the explorer to choose the method by which he will be killed. The explorer is asked to make a single statement. If it is true he will be thrown off a high cliff. If it is false he will be eaten by lions. What clever statement does the explorer make that forces the chief to let him go?

41. Animal Madness

Can you name the creature missing from the nursery rhyme?

1. Mary had a little _lamb_

2. With a nicknack paddywhack, give the _dog_ a bone.

3. Pop goes the _wesle_

4. The _cow_ jumped over the moon.

42. Wise Words

What is the one thing that all people, no matter how important they are, agree is between heaven and earth?

43. Gambling Games

Tom and Nancy are playing a game of cards for £1 a game. At the end of the evening, Tom has won three games and Nancy has won £3. How many games did they play?

44. Put Them Together

Match up these characters with their other halves.

Gretel   Jane   Hermione Granger   Gandalf   Jerry

Harry Potter   Bilbo Baggins   Tom   Tarzan   Hansel

45. About Turn

A group of soldiers were standing in the boiling hot sun, facing west. Their sergeant shouted at them: "Right Turn! About Turn! Left Turn!" What direction are they now facing? Right and left turns are both 90 degrees, and an about turn is 180 degrees.

46. Complete the Sequence

What's the next letter in the list?

M T W T

47. Car Trouble

A four-wheeled car has travelled 24,000 km and uses four tyres. How far has each separate tyre travelled?

48. Wacky Wordsearch

N	B	E	R	R	A	Z	I	B	M	F	C
J	P	U	V	I	Q	P	L	G	R	R	A
R	T	W	O	S	H	S	H	E	K	U	O
Q	D	F	G	N	N	A	K	E	B	D	D
A	B	C	M	I	G	J	G	G	T	E	M
Y	T	Z	F	E	J	N	P	G	N	S	Q
K	S	H	K	L	A	S	C	D	H	J	G
C	D	V	U	R	R	S	M	B	H	P	Z
A	O	N	T	D	S	H	O	A	W	N	H
W	M	S	S	W	T	B	F	Q	I	S	D
P	J	I	D	E	H	V	Z	R	D	K	D
C	W	W	E	I	R	D	M	U	B	G	O

Find the words:

STRANGE
WACKY
ODD
WEIRD
BIZARRE
RUDE

49. Number Solver

Find two whole numbers which, when multiplied together, give an answer of 61.

50. What am I?

You use me from head to toe, the more I work the thinner I grow. What am I?

HAND

sand

send

seed

feed

FEET

51. Letter Game

Go from HAND to FEET by changing only one letter at a time.

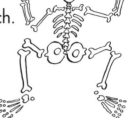

1. This is found on a beach.
2. You do this to a letter.
3. You plant this to make a flower grow.
4. To take food in.

52. Picture Puzzle

Work out the saying from the picture.

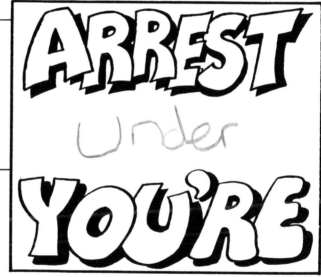

ARREST
under
YOU'RE

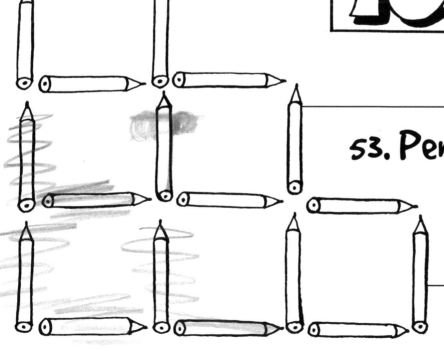

53. Pencil Palaver

Take away six pencils to leave three equal-sized squares.

54. Sweet Tooth

Five children were sharing out a box of sweets. Bob took five, Peter took five, Joey took five and Danny took five. That left half the pack, which Natasha took. How many sweets were there altogether?

20

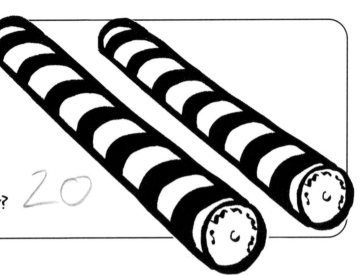

FLUFF
IRAQI
ROBIN
SANTA
TOTAL

55. Long List

What's special about the list of words opposite? (Clue: look at the beginning and end of each word.)

56. Number Parts

Bill's number is two, Clare's number is three and Edward's number is five. What is Donna's number?

57. Body Parts

Name ten body parts that are spelt with three letters. No slang words!

58. Pictionary

Work out the saying from the picture.

The time after Time

59. Chocolate Challenge

One boy can eat sixteen chocolates in half a minute, and another can eat half as many in twice the length of time. How many chocolates can both boys eat between them in fifteen seconds?

10

60. Common Factor

What letter do the following numbers have in common?

3, 7, 10, 11, 12

61. Sleep Tight

Turn the word SLEEP into DREAM by changing one letter at a time.

1. An alarm clock makes this noise.
2. What happens when you cut yourself.
3. A species of something.
4. Eat this with jam.
5. Not looking forward to something.

SLEEP

bleep
bleed
breed
bread
dread

DREAM

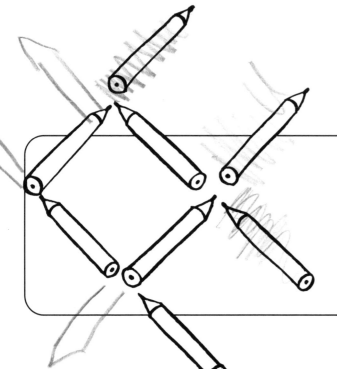

62. Sink or Swim

Reposition three pencils to make the fish swim in the opposite direction.

IKLN

63. Picture Guess

Discover the saying from the picture.

64. Memory Trick

Pick a number between one and ten. Multiply by nine. Subtract five. Add the digits together and repeat this step until you have a one-digit number. For whatever number you have, pick that letter of the alphabet. E.g. A = 1, B = 2, etc.
Now think of a country beginning with that letter.
Think of an animal that begins with the second letter of the country.
Think of a colour usually associated with the animal. What do you have?

65. A Dog's Life

Once there was a dog named Nelly, who lived on a farm. There were three other dogs on the farm. Their names were Blackie, Whitey and Brownie. What do you think the fourth dog's name was?

Nelly

66. Anagram Anger

Rearrange these letters to give the title of a famous wizard.

PORT TRAY HER

HARRY POTTER

67. Memorise This

Look at the picture for one minute. Then cover it up – no cheating! – and answer the questions.

1. How many loaves of bread are there in the bakery window? *4*
2. Whose bakery is it? *Benies*
3. What hairstyles do the twins have? *same*
4. What time is it? *1030*
5. Is the toy shop closed or open? *open*

68. Odd One Out

Which of the following words doesn't belong in the group and why?

LAME   MALE   MEAL   MEAT

69. Building Split

This row of ten letters can be split into two five-letter words which are the names of two things used to make buildings. Words read from left to right and the letters are in the correct order. What are they?

B R S I T O C K N E

~~BRICK~~ Brick stone

70. Visual Aid

Guess the saying from the visual aid.

Ready For more

71. Ridiculous Riddle

What goes up and down the stairs without moving?

The carpet

72. Snakes Alive

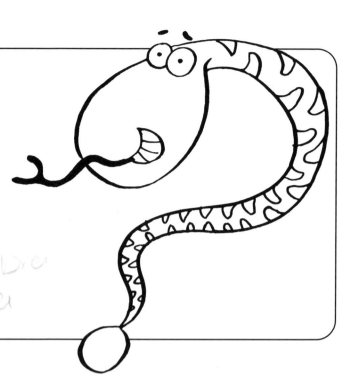

The name of a type of snake is hidden in each of the sentences below. Find them by joining words or parts of words together.

1. How sad Derek looks. *Adder*
2. They stayed all night at the disco, bravely in my opinion. *Kobra*
3. The jumbo arrived on time. *Boa*

73. Flower Power

Here are the names of four flowers with the vowels removed. Can you name them?

DSY   BTTRCP   DFFDL   SNFLWR

74. Hunt the Word

The letters missing from this box make up the name of an animal. Can you name it?

bear

ABE

75. Happy Birthday

Sally was eight the day before yesterday.

Next year she will be ten.

What is the date of Sally's birthday, and on which date would the first two things have been true?

5ᵗʰ of December (handwritten)

76. Tennis Trouble

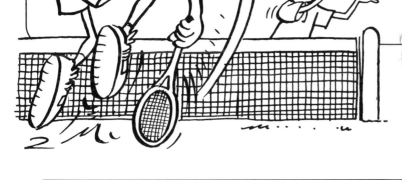

Two men were playing tennis. They played five sets and and each man won three sets. How can this be possible? *The two men were playing doubles* (handwritten)

77. Spoon Puzzle

Reposition six of the spoons in the pattern to make six equal-sized diamond shapes in a star pattern.

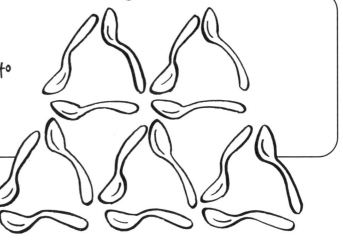

78. What's Next?

What's the next letter in the series?

B, C, D, E, G, P

they all ryme

79. What is It?

Guess the phrase from the picture.

Me right

right beside me

80. Tall Tale

Before Mount Everest was discovered, what was the tallest mountain in the world?

Mount Everest

81. Maths Magic

Is half of two plus two equal to two or three?

three

82. Give me Five

Solve the clues, so that each answer contains five letters. Write all the answers in place and the shaded dashes reading down will reveal the name of a musical instrument.

1. Opposite of last.
2. Outer covering of an egg.
3. Sailing boat.
4. Bad weather.
5. Light you can carry.
6. Push this to power a bicycle.
7. Meadow.
8. Number in a trio.

1. f i r s t
2. s h e l l
3. y a c h t
4. c l o u d
5. t o r c h
6. p e d a l
7. f i e l d
8. t h r e e

recorder

83. Word Mix

Rearrange the letters of GROW NO LINSEED to spell one single word.

GROW NO
LINSEED

one single word

84. Word Ladder

Change NOSE into FAST by changing one letter at a time.

1. Misplace.
2. Opposite of found.
3. At the back.

NOSE

lose

lost

last

FAST

85. Big is Best

Who is bigger? Mr Bigger, Mrs Bigger or their baby?

baby

86. The Hole Truth

If it takes three people to dig a hole, how many people does it take to dig half a hole?

cant dig half a hole

87. Mathematical Equation

If five thousand, five hundred and five pounds is written as £5,505, how should twelve thousand, twelve hundred and twelve pounds be written?

13,212

88. Matchstick Marvel

Reposition four matches from this pattern to form five triangles.

89. Finish it off

What is the last letter needed to complete this sequence?

O, T, T, F, F, S, S, E, N T

90. How Confusing

What starts with a T, ends with a T
and has T in it?

Teapot

91. What am I?

My first is in chair
But isn't in chain

My second is in pale
And also in pain

My third is in edge
But isn't in green

 R
A
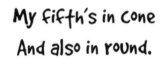 D
I
O

My fourth is in lime
But isn't in mean

My fifth's in cone
And also in round.

Do you know what I am?
I'm connected with sound!

92. Hot or Cold?

What moves faster, heat or cold?

Heat

93. Maths Trick

When can you add two to eleven and get one?

94. Word Scramble

Rearrange these letters to give the names of some animals you might find at the zoo.

Panda

DANAP

KNOMEY

Monkey

elephant

NAHPETLE

FEIRAGF

giraffe

95. Work it Out

If two hours ago, it was exactly as long after one o'clock in the afternoon as it was before one o'clock in the morning, what time would it be now?

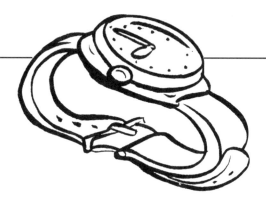
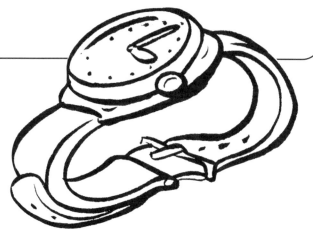

96. Animal Tracks

Make tracks and find seven different animals in the grid. Start at the letter in the top left square and move in any direction except diagonally. Every letter is used once.

```
C A M E A R
L L E B L E
I A R D E P
O P E G I H
N O R E T A
L E A P T N
```

97. Take Away

What is it that, when you take away the whole, you still have some left over?

98. Perplexing Puzzle

What is in the middle of nowhere?

99. Bowling

Four friends go bowling together. They decide that they will each play each other once.
How many games will they play? *six games*

100. Fitting In

What is the only other letter that fits in the following series?

B, C, D, E, I, K, O, X, *+H*

101. Key Words

There's a problem on the keyboard of Clare's computer. She types in letters but the screen only shows numbers! In each case the letter links to a number below it.
So, for example, a 1 can stand for a Q, an A or a Z.
The number 9 could be an O or an L.
Can you work out what Clare was trying to say?

```
1 2 3 4 5 6 7 8 9 0
Q W E R T Y U I O P
A S D F G H J K L
Z X C V B N M
```

I w…
8 2165 5682 7136863
59 53 43018433

I WON THE MONEY
to be PICPONE

ANSWERS

1. Paintbrush Puzzle

2. Logic Puzzler

Your age.

3. Anagram Antics

Scissors

Hammer

Parrot

Doctor

4. Number Search

13 and 19

5. Baffling Bet

The man is in a no-win situation –
even if he wins the bet he still loses
£1 of his money.

6. Word Play

Pork
Slow
Card

7. Age Question

She's twelve.

8. Number Cross

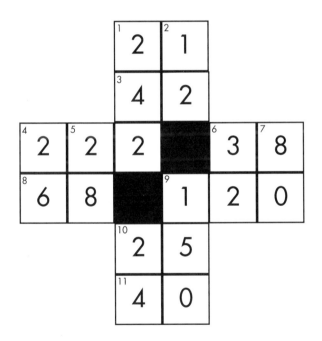

9. Driving Dilemma

Bill was driving in reverse.

10. Wild Wordsearch

M	D	Y	T	A	F	W	U	Q	D	J	P
K	O	I	R	C	E	S	H	O	Z	K	S
T	B	U	J	O	C	I	G	L	B	D	Y
A	Z	Y	S	K	V	S	O	B	C	W	E
O	A	C	N	E	C	F	X	Y	I	N	K
C	I	L	K	F	S	N	A	C	R	N	N
F	O	S	J	E	T	D	D	O	F	L	O
H	R	C	A	W	I	B	K	S	I	Q	M
I	P	R	Q	U	X	N	T	H	P	L	X
K	I	Y	T	E	R	E	S	R	O	H	A
G	T	D	A	Z	C	I	O	J	U	C	B
R	W	A	C	F	L	X	B	D	R	I	B

11. Letter Change

1. REEL
2. FEEL
3. FEET
4. FELT

12. Number Sequence

Fourteen – each time you add on two, then one, then two, then one and so on.

13. Ridiculous Riddle

Coal

14. Alphabet Puzzle

1. Hair
2. Fair
3. Chair

15. Letter Assembler

Everything

16. What am I?

Empty

17. Mix and Match

Swan + cygnet
Bear + cub
Cow + calf
Kangaroo + joey
Rooster + chick
Horse + foal

18. Spot the Difference

1. The bottle of drink has gone.
2. The woman's glasses have disappeared.
3. There are now only two balloons.
4. There are only four people queuing
   for ice cream now.
5. There are five birds in the air now.

19. Solve the Mystery

They were used to make a snowman.
The snow has melted.

20. Word Change

1. Tale
2. Date
3. Nine or Five

21. Proverb Puzzler

Strike while the iron is hot

22. Number Cruncher

TWENTY NINE

23. Word Wizz

1. IRIS   2. ROSE
3. ASTER   4. VIOLET

24. Pencil Trick

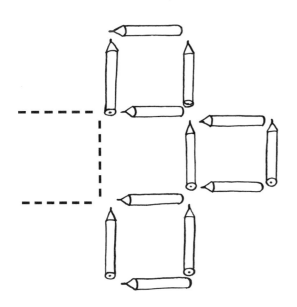

25. Letter Logic

S O N D – they are all the first letters of months of the year

26. Countdown Conundrum

21

27. Hidden Countries

1. Canada – Our dog likes his food so much he eats a **can a d**ay.
2. India – Always use a pencil when drawing lines **in dia**grams.
3. Spain – The king was angry when a thief stole hi**s pain**ting.
4. China – Does the teacher tea**ch in a** classroom?
5. Germany – In an**ger, many** people say things they don't mean.

28. Adder

Moored

29. Tricky Words

They can all have the word BREAK in front of them to make a new word.

30. How Did She Do That?

It wasn't raining.

31. Upside Down

68 (changes to 89)

32. Learn the Language

The key sentences are: There are only three words in the English language. What is the third word? The third word is 'language'.

33. Match them Up

34. Mind the Gap

For

35. Oddly Enough

Out!

36. Figure it Out

He had six apples to start with and ate two apples on the first day and two on the second.

37. Date Dilemma

32 – including both dates.

38. Missing Alphabet

K and R

39. Catch a Cat

Six cats

40. Deadly Decision

The explorer makes the statement: "I will be killed by the lions". Now if the chief feeds him to the lions, his statement will be true, so he should be thrown off the cliff. But if he is thrown off the cliff, his statement will be false. The chief has to let the explorer go!

41. Animal Madness

1. Lamb
2. Dog
3. Weasel
4. Cow

42. Wise Words

AND is between heaven and earth.

43. Gambling Games

They played nine games. Tom won three games and Nancy won six games.

44. Put Them Together

Hansel and Gretel
Tarzan and Jane
Harry Potter and Hermione Granger
Tom and Jerry
Bilbo Baggins and Gandalf

45. About Turn

East

46. Complete the Sequence

The next letter is F – the days of the week.

47. Car Trouble

They all travelled the same distance – 24,000 km each.

48. Wacky Wordsearch

N	B	E	R	R	A	Z	I	B	M	F	C
J	P	U	V	I	Q	P	L	G	R	R	A
R	T	W	O	S	H	S	H	E	K	U	O
Q	D	F	G	N	N	A	K	E	B	D	D
A	B	C	M	I	G	J	G	G	T	E	M
Y	T	Z	F	E	J	N	P	G	N	S	Q
K	S	H	K	L	A	S	C	D	H	J	G
C	D	V	U	R	R	S	M	B	H	P	Z
A	O	N	T	D	S	H	O	A	W	N	H
W	M	S	S	W	T	B	F	Q	I	S	D
P	J	I	D	E	H	V	Z	R	D	K	D
C	W	W	E	I	R	D	M	U	B	G	O

49. Number Solver

1 x 61

50. What am I?

A bar of soap.

51. Letter Game

1. Sand
2. Send
3. Seed
4. Feed

52. Picture Puzzle

You're under arrest.

53. Pencil Palaver

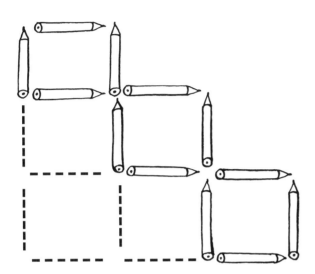

54. Sweet Tooth

40

55. Long List

The first letters in sequence, spell FIRST, the final letters spell FINAL.

56. Number Parts

Four – the first letter of the name has a value with A = 1, B = 2, etc.

57. Body Parts

Arm, Ear, Eye, Gum, Hip, Jaw, Lip, Leg, Rib, Toe.
Not: Bum, Gut, Lap!

58. Pictionary

Time after time

59. Chocolate Challenge

Ten chocolates

60. Common Factor

The only vowel they contain when written out fully is the letter E.

61. Sleep Tight

1. Bleep
2. Bleed
3. Breed
4. Bread
5. Dread

62. Sink or Swim

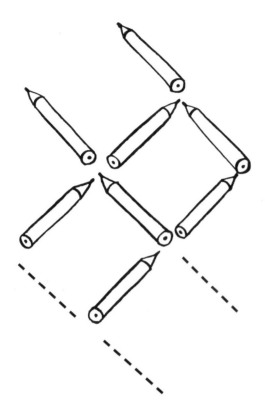

63. Picture Guess

Missing Link

64. Memory Trick

Do you have a grey elephant from Denmark? Now try it on your friends!

65. A Dog's Life

Nelly

66. Anagram Anger

Harry Potter

67. Memorise This

1. Four
2. Bernie's
3. Plaits
4. 10.30 am
5. Open

68. Odd One Out

Meat – all the others are anagrams of each other.

69. Building Split

Brick and Stone

70. Visual Aid

Ready for more.

71. Ridiculous Riddle

A carpet

72. Snakes Alive

1. Adder
2. Cobra
3. Boa

73. Flower Power

1. Daisy
2. Buttercup
3. Daffodil
4. Sunflower

74. Hunt the Word

Bear

75. Happy Birthday

Sally's birthday is 31st December. The information would have been true on 1st January.

76. Tennis Trouble

The two men were partners playing doubles.

77. Spoon Puzzle

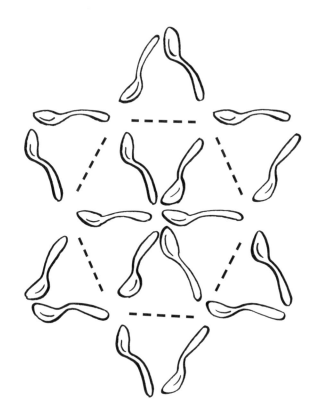

78. What's Next?

P – they all rhyme.

79. What is It?

Right beside me

80. Tall Tale

Mount Everest – it was the tallest mountain even before it was discovered!

81. Maths Magic

Three

82. Give me five

1. First
2. Shell
3. Yacht
4. Storm
5. Torch
6. Pedal
7. Field
8. Three

The musical instrument made
is a RECORDER

83. Word Mix

ONE SINGLE WORD

84. Word Ladder

1. Lose
2. Lost
3. Last

85. Big is Best

The baby, because he's a
little bigger!

86. The Hole Truth

You can't dig half a hole!

87. Mathematical Equation

£13,212

88. Matchstick Marvel

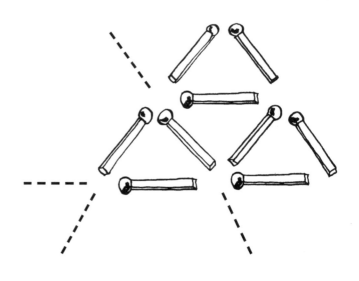

89. Finish it off

T – the letters are the initials of the numbers one to ten.

90. How Confusing

A teapot

91. What am I?

Radio

92. Hot or Cold

Heat – everyone can catch a cold!

93. Maths Trick

When you add two hours to eleven o'clock you get one o'clock.

94. Word Scramble

Elephant
Panda
Giraffe
Monkey

95. Work it out

Nine o'clock – since there are twelve hours between the two times, and half of that time equals six, then the halfway mark would have to be seven o'clock.
If it were seven o'clock, two hours ago, then the time would now be nine o'clock.

96. Animal Tracks

1. Camel
2. Lion
3. Leopard
4. Bear
5. Elephant
6. Tiger
7. Ape

97. Take Away

The word 'wholesome'.

98. Perplexing Puzzle

The Letter 'H'.

99. Bowling

There are six games.

100. Fitting In

H – all of the letters in the series flipped vertically look the same.

101. Key Words

I WANT THIS MACHINE TO BE REPAIRED.

Now that you've completed 101 of our brainbender puzzles it's time to find out what your score reveals about your brain's puzzle-solving ability!

1–20	You have an average puzzle solving ability.
21–40	Your performance reveals that you are a fine puzzle solver.
41–60	People with this score are often distinguished puzzle busters.
61–80	Your logical thinking makes problem solving easy.
81–101	Puzzle master – puzzles are easy for your fabulous brain.